by Daphne Greaves
illustrated by Michael Sloan

Requests for permission to make copies of any part of the work should be addressed to School Permissions and Copyrights, Harcourt, Inc., 6277 Sea Harbor Drive, Orlando, Florida 32887-6777. Fax: 407-345-2418.

Printed in China

ISBN 10: 0-15-350527-3
ISBN 13: 978-0-15-350527-0

Ordering Options
ISBN 10: 0-15-350334-3 (Grade 4 Below-Level Collection)
ISBN 13: 978-0-15-350334-4 (Grade 4 Below-Level Collection)
ISBN 10: 0-15-357519-0 (package of 5)
ISBN 13: 978-0-15-357519-8 (package of 5)

4 5 6 7 8 9 10 0940 12 11 10 09

Characters

Narrator 1	Chris	Lisa	Mom
Narrator 2	Luke	Amy	

Setting: Luke and Lisa's house

Narrator 1: It was a dark and stormy day.

Narrator 2: Look at that lightning! This weather is miserable.

Narrator 1: Actually, the thunder and lightning make a perfect backdrop for our play.

Narrator 2: That's true since the play is a mystery about lightning.

Narrator 1: It's about twins named Luke and Lisa.

Narrator 2: Luke is an amateur magician, and Lisa is an amateur detective.

Narrator 1: Luke is good at performing magic tricks. He likes to challenge Lisa to figure out his tricks. Today Luke has a new trick.

Narrator 1: He told Lisa that she won't be able to figure out this one!

Narrator 2: Their friends, Chris and Amy, are waiting out the storm at Luke and Lisa's house. They've gathered in the game room to watch Luke perform.

Chris: What have you got for us today, Luke, a new card trick?

Luke: I have something more spectacular than that.

Lisa: I bet it's a coin trick. Luke's been trying to perfect his coin tricks lately.

Amy: If you pull any coins out of my ears, may I keep them?

Luke: Sorry, Amy, no coin tricks today.

Chris: I bet you're doing the exotic Persian rope trick.

Luke: No, my performance today is a force of nature!

Narrator 1: Just then a bolt of lightning flashed outside the window. Thunder exploded loudly.

Narrator 2: Luke smiles at the little group. He beams self-assurance as he points to the window.

Luke: Just like that!

Amy: What?

Luke: Lightning! I used to call myself Luke the Magnificent. Now I am Luke Lightning Bolt!

Lisa: Wait a minute. Are you saying that the storm is your magic trick?

Luke: No, I'm saying that I can create lightning right here indoors.

Narrator 1: Luke has a small platform that he installed to use as a stage for his performances.

Narrator 2: Luke jumps onto the platform and confidently faces his audience.

Luke: Today I will confound and amaze you. However, first I'd like to tell you a story about how I learned to do this awesome trick.

Narrator 2: Everyone in the audience gives Luke their full attention.

Luke: One afternoon, I took a walk. I was deep in thought, so I didn't notice the ominous clouds looming overhead. Suddenly, a flash of lightning pierced the clouds in the distance.

Narrator 1: At that moment, lightning slashes the sky outside the window, and Luke's audience jumps with fright.

Luke: Like you, I was roused by the startling power of the storm. As I hurried home, I tripped on something blown by the wind. I inadvertently trampled it and stumbled. When I looked up I saw an enormous flash of lightning. Since that moment, I have been able to create lightning.

Narrator I: Chris stares at Luke, his mouth hanging open with awe.

Chris: Wow, that is amazing!

Lisa: Yes, but not much of a magic trick.

Luke: Then get ready for magic right now. Amy, please close the window curtains, and turn out the lights.

Amy: Sure.

Lisa: How am I supposed to monitor what you're doing in the dark?

Luke: Sorry, the lightning shows up much better in the dark.

Amy: Let's turn out the lights and see the trick.

Lisa: Okay.

Narrator 1: The room is pitch-black as Luke begins to speak.

Luke: Lightning flashes, and thunder booms. *Abracadabra, sim sala soom!* Lightning appears in this very room!

Narrator 2: Suddenly, a tiny spark of light dances in the air.

Chris: Look at that!

Narrator 2: Lisa jumps up and turns on the lights.

Luke: Pretty neat, huh?

Narrator 1: Lisa and Luke's mother knocks on the game-room door.

Narrator 2: Their mom is a very gracious hostess. She always offers the kids milk and a snack.

Mom: Who wants peanut butter sandwiches?

Narrator 1: Lisa hangs back as the others head to the kitchen. Something has caught her eye.

Narrator 2: It is sticking out from under the stage. Lisa bends down and picks it up.

Narrator 1: It is a pie tin with a foam handle attached to it. There is also another piece of foam.

Narrator 1: Lisa begins to tinker with the objects. She knows Luke must have used them to perform his trick. She just can't figure out how.

Narrator 2: Soon, Lisa joins the others in the kitchen.

Mom: There you are. I was beginning to think you weren't participating in snack time.

Luke: No, Mom, Lisa was just trying to figure out my magic trick, but she can't.

Mom: I wouldn't be so sure, Luke. Your sister is very resourceful.

Narrator 1: Suddenly, Luke's mother reaches up and brushes back his hair.

Mom: Luke, your hair needs combing.

Narrator 2: Lisa looks at Luke's untidy hair. She jumps up.

Lisa: I've got it! I've exposed Luke's trick!

Narrator 1: Back in the game room, Lisa stands on Luke's stage. She holds up the pie tin and foam.

Lisa: I am now going to rub the foam very rapidly against my hair. Now, watch as I hold the pie tin by its handle over the foam. Next, I touch the pie tin with the tip of my finger.

Narrator 2: A spark of electricity appears.

Chris: Cool!

Amy: How does it work?

Lisa: It's static electricity.

Luke: That's right. When you rub the foam on your hair, electrons from your hair pile up on it.

Lisa: Place the pie tin over the foam, and its electrons pull on the electrons in the tin. When you touch the pie tin with your finger, the electrons moving around in the tin leap to your hand!

Luke: That's what makes the spark.

Chris: Our very own tiny lightning bolt!

Luke: Good job, Lisa!

Amy: Hey, look! It stopped raining.

Narrator 1: Before you can say *abracadabra*—the group is outside enjoying a sunny day.

Think Critically

1. The narrators say that it is a stormy day and that Luke is good at magic tricks. Which of these statements is a fact? Which is an opinion?

2. What is the theme, or subject, of this Readers' Theater?

3. How are Lisa and Luke alike? How are they different?

4. Which clue finally helped Lisa solve the mystery?

5. If you could be any character in this play, who would you be? Why?

Science

Static Electricity Look in a reference book or on the Internet to find out more about static electricity. Then write two or three sentences describing what you discovered.

School-Home Connection With family members, think of some tricks you have seen performed. Discuss what the secrets behind the tricks might be.

Word Count: 1,001